The Gr[illegible]
Study Guide for
Teens

A Bible Study for Teenagers on the C.S. Lewis Book *The Great Divorce*

By Alan Vermilye

"If we insist on keeping Hell (or even earth) we shall not see Heaven: if we accept Heaven we shall not be able to retain even the smallest and most intimate souvenirs of Hell."
The Great Divorce

The Great Divorce Study Guide for Teens
A Bible Study for Teenagers
on the C.S. Lewis Book
The Great Divorce

ISBN-13: 978-1-948481-00-7

To learn more about this Bible study, order additional copies, or to download the answer guide visit www.BrownChairBooks.com

Version 1

Table of Contents

Introduction

I recently read a story about a man who has visited Disneyland every day since 2012. Now, more than five years later he has gone through the turnstiles 2,000 days in a row! I love Disney theme parks too, but that's commitment!

What about you? Could you visit the "happiest place on Earth" 2,000 days straight? What would you have to sacrifice in your life to do so?

In *The Great Divorce* by C.S. Lewis, damned spirits from Hell take a celestial bus ride to visit Heaven. Once there, they are invited by people they formerly knew—relatives and friends—to stay forever.

Sounds like the opportunity of a lifetime, right? I mean, who wants to go back to a dark and dingy Hell when you're in the ultimate Disney Park ever! So, what's the catch?

It's really quite simple. You must honestly admit that you're wrong (repent of your sins) and then choose to do right (follow Jesus). Sounds easy enough, but is it really?

That's the hardest part about sin—to admit you're wrong. It can often be very hard to let go of what is dragging you down and instead embrace a better life that God has planned for you.

This story is not to be taken literally. Scripture records no bus-riding opportunities offering free passes into Heaven after death. The fact is, Hell is final. On the title page, you will find the following quote: "No, there is no escape. There is no heaven with a little of hell in it—no plan to retain this or that of the devil in our hearts or our pockets. Out Satan must go, every hair and feather."

Everyone you meet in life is soul searching and their efforts either move them toward or away from God. As hard as it is to leave your old life of sin behind, it does get a little easier with each step. But you have to take that first step.

This is a fun book to read but also a bit challenging at times. Hang in there, take your time, and write notes in your book and in this study book. Most importantly, try to participate in a group discussion with others your age and with an adult leader.

I believe at the end of reading the book and completing this study, you will have a renewed passion for following Christ as well as getting rid of those things in your life that are dragging you down.

Book Summary

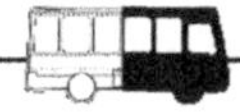

Although this summary does not include every detail of the book, it does provide an overview of the story. For that reason, if, like a great movie, you do not want the end spoiled, I encourage you to skip this summary and move on to reading the book.

In *The Great Divorce*, by all accounts, Lewis is the narrator guiding us through a series of events beginning with his waiting in a long line for a magical bus ride in a dismally uncomforting grey town—which is in fact Hell or Purgatory.

Those waiting with him in the bus line are argumentative, combative, and generally disagreeable and of differing economic and educational backgrounds. These unpleasant and contentious souls take vacations to visit other places outside of Hell. Most visit Earth, while a few others will make this bus trip to the outer banks of Heaven.

As they board and the bus leaves the ground, Lewis begins talking with others aboard about the grey town—this seedy and empty city that stretches on forever and where time seems to be paused. He learns that in the grey town evening never advances to night; it's dreary, dull, dirty, and bleak, and it's always raining. It is a place, for all its vastness, that seems empty, with very few people wandering around.

In addition, there are no communities since the residents of the grey town are constantly spreading throughout the town because they cannot stand to be with each other. Some, after being there for centuries, have actually moved lightyears away from the bus stop, which prevents them from making the long journey back.

The residents in the grey town get everything they want, but not of great quality, by simply imagining it. They can think structures, homes, and other things into existence, but nothing is able to meet their basic needs. For example, if one desires a house, it is there, but it will not keep out the rain or danger. For this reason, they venture off to build new houses, and the town continues to spread.

The bus flies for hours through darkness until it approaches a beautiful countryside. As the travelers exit the bus, some become overwhelmed and retreat back to the safety of the bus, while others, braver, huddle together and press forward into the vast, beautiful unknown.

The landscape, including the grass, flowers, mountains, etc., is all beautiful in appearance, but it is also solid and heavy so that the blades of grass are as sharp and hard as diamonds and cause terrible pain just to walk on. Even a single leaf is too heavy to lift.

Soon the Ghosts are approached by the resident Spirits of Heaven, who are filled with a great light; they are very grand and seemingly ageless. Some are naked, some are robed, and others have beards, but all are muscular with smooth flesh, and the earth shakes underneath their feet as they are solid, not transparent like the Ghosts from the grey town.

The Spirits are relatives and friends the Ghosts formerly knew on earth. They encourage the Ghosts to abandon the grey town and come with them up the mountain to enjoy the bliss of Heaven. Each Spirit is gentle but also direct in helping the Ghosts recognize their sin and their need for redemption. The Ghosts are assured that as they leave behind their pride, hatred, and unbelief and progress toward the mountain with the Spirits, it will get easier as they will begin to feel more solid.

Unfortunately, the majority of the Ghosts refuse and return to the grey town, retaining their own independence rather than submitting themselves to God.

After witnessing a variety of conversations between Ghosts and Spirits, Lewis realizes that each Ghost represents a character study of human nature and the struggle with sin. In fact, many of their sins are not what we might consider evil or diabolical, yet they still are unable to enter Heaven. This leaves Lewis confused, miserable, and somewhat fearful.

At last, he is approached by his guiding Spirit—author, poet, and Christian minister George MacDonald. MacDonald answers Lewis's most pressing questions regarding the fate of the Ghosts he finds himself with, including, "Do any of them stay? Can they stay? Is any real choice offered to them? How do they come to be here?"

In the end, MacDonald finally confirms to Lewis that he is dreaming. As the sun begins to rise in Lewis's dream, he becomes both surprised and terrified of remaining a Ghost as day breaks in Heaven. At this point, he awakens to books falling on his head.

Through his journey, Lewis is convinced of the goodness and mercy of God as well as his own need and the urgency for redemption.

Character Summary

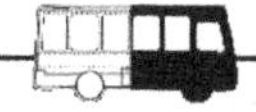

LEWIS / PROTAGONIST/ NARRATOR

The story is written in the first person with the narrator never being identified by name but implied as being C.S. Lewis. His character is both a learned man and drawn to literary giants like George MacDonald, whose writings had an impact on Lewis's life. For this reason, throughout the study guide, we will refer to the narrator as Lewis.

In the story, Lewis is primarily an observer of the other Ghosts and their discussions with the Spirit Guides. It is through these discourses that he comes to understand the deceptive nature of sin and the grip it has on human nature and our seeming inability to let it go—even when given the opportunity for infinite joy.

THE SPIRIT GUIDES

The Spirit Guides are residents of Heaven who have been glorified after death through their trust and faith in Jesus Christ. Each Spirit approaches a Ghost he or she had a relationship with during their earthly life. They encourage the Ghosts to abandon the grey town and to come up with them to the mountain to enjoy the bliss of Heaven. The Spirits are gentle but also direct in helping the Ghosts recognize their sin and need for redemption. The majority of the Ghosts view the Spirits as being antagonistic and therefore refuse their offer and abandon Heaven, not wanting to confront their sin.

GEORGE MACDONALD

Lewis's guiding spirit is none other than author, poet, and Christian minister George MacDonald, whose works include *Phantastes, The Princess and the Goblin*, and *At the Back of the North Wind.* MacDonald's work had a profound influence on Lewis during his earthly life and, in this story, serves as a father figure and mentor type in the afterlife helping Lewis to understand the ways of Heaven.

THE TOUSEL-HAIRED POET

The tousle-haired poet feels unappreciated by most everyone he meets. His distaste for capitalism drives him to communism and eventually to becoming a conscientious objector due to his disdain for war. He has an excessive desire for attention and need for respect from others that leaves him feeling like the victim when he does not receive any. His self-pity is so strong that he ended his life by throwing himself under a train, not desiring to live in a world that was against him.

IKEY (THE INTELLIGENT GHOST)

The Intelligent Ghost is a thriving entrepreneur. He does not believe the problem in the grey town is that people quarrel but rather that they have no needs. His solution is to travel to Heaven and bring back, or steal, "some real commodities," or saleable goods, that would generate demand. This foolish attempt to profit from Heaven leaves him battered and bruised, unable to lift any solid apples to take back with him.

FAT GHOST (WITH GAITERS)

The Fat Ghost believes the old theology of Hell and judgment are outdated superstitions and what the inhabitants of the town really need is spirituality unencumbered by any materialism and matter. In fact, he is unaware that the grey town he has inhabited is Hell until the Spirit he encounters reveals him as an apostate living in Hell. His sin is of the intellect since he has embraced liberal theology and rejected the resurrection of Christ for success and position within the church.

THE BIG GHOST

This man is astonished and outraged to find Len, the Guiding Spirit he encounters, enjoying life in Heaven. He recognizes Len only as an earthly murderer and cannot understand why Len is here in Heaven and he himself is in the grey town since he believes he was a much better man on Earth. Len does his best to persuade the Big Ghost to acknowledge his faults, but he wants no part of a Heaven that allows murderers to become citizens.

THE HARD-BITTEN GHOST

During his earthly life, this man traveled much of the world, building only a cynical view of what he experienced. He is suspicious, does not trust anyone, and develops conspiracies about most everything, including Heaven and Hell. He says that he knows all about Heaven and that it's the same old lie he's heard all his life.

THE WELL-DRESSED GHOST

During both her earthly life and in the afterlife, this woman's vanity drives her to become completely self-absorbed, if not ashamed, and unable to see anyone but herself. In an attempt to shake her from this preoccupation with self, the attending Spirit calls a herd of unicorns to create some sort of diversion that would draw her mind away from herself and to God.

THE SCIENTIST GHOST

MacDonald tells Lewis of this ghost whose scientific research consumed his life; he eventually died and made it to the outskirts of Heaven. He decided not to continue on to the mountains because there was nothing in Heaven left to prove, no question that he could provide an answer for. He could not overcome his disappointment and simply accept God as "a little child and [enter] into joy."

THE GRUMBLING GHOST

This female ghost has allowed occasional complaining and grumbling to become full-fledged sin that has consumed her life. MacDonald assures Lewis, who thinks she's just a silly old woman who has gotten into a bad habit, that if there's a spark of the woman left, she can be saved.

THE SENSUAL GHOST

This ghost is completely self-consumed with her appearance, believing she can seduce the Spirits with her body and completely unaware that her body is no longer substantial or enticing.

THE FAMOUS ARTIST GHOST

The Artist Ghost was quite famous on Earth and had begun painting as a means to tell about the light, but over time he lost that desire and just painted for painting sake. He now finds himself interested only in painting God's creation but not actually interested in God Himself. He is encouraged by his Spirit Guide to drink from a fountain that will cause him to forget all of his earthly works and create an appreciation of all work without false modesty or pride.

THE OVERBEARING WIFE GHOST

This ghost is hypocritical, depressing, critical, and self-centered. She is extremely controlling of her husband, Robert, and treats him more like her property, having nagged him to death in their earthly life. Her self-image rests solely on the actions of others—specifically that of her husband.

THE MOTHERLY GHOST

Disappointed to be greeted in Heaven by her brother, Reginald, this Motherly Ghost had made an idol of her love for her son, Michael. Her desire to see her son is stronger than her desire for God and is ultimately what prevents her from growing solid and continuing into Heaven.

THE OILY GHOST AND HIS LIZARD

This Ghost is described as a "dark and oily" smoke with a little red lizard sitting on its shoulder that is constantly touching its tail and whispering in the Ghost's ear. The lizard is the embodiment of some type of lust. The Ghost thinks he can keep it under control, at least in the polite company of Heaven, but he cannot. The Spirit offers to kill the lizard but says he is only free to do so with the Ghost's consent.

SARAH SMITH

MacDonald refers to Sarah Smith as "one of the great ones." She's beautiful, warm, loving, and seemingly capable of infinite kindness. In the afterlife, Sarah has a large "family" because on Earth, she was kind and gracious to many different people, even people whom she barely knew. On Earth, Sarah and the dwarf, whose name is Frank, were married, and she preceded him in death. Although not famous on Earth, in Heaven, Sarah is a saint. Lewis picks the name Sarah Smith for this very reason—to emphasize her plainness.

FRANK THE DWARF GHOST AND THE TRAGEDIAN

Frank has a "divided nature" split between two figures, the Dwarf and the Tragedian—an old-school, melodramatic actor who specializes in tragic roles. The real Frank is the "Dwarf," who becomes less and less himself the more he feeds his persona or alter ego, the Tragedian, who projects the dwarf's need to be pitied and apologized to.

MacDonald elaborates on other types of Ghosts that come near to Heaven but do not stay:

TEACHING GHOSTS

The most common was the type that wanted to tell, teach, or lecture the Celestials on Hell.

TUB-THUMPING GHOSTS

A tub-thumper is a noisy, violent, or ranting public speaker—the radical revolutionaries demanding that the Spirits rise up and free themselves from "happiness," tear down the mountains, and "seize Heaven for their own."

PLANNING GHOSTS

These Ghosts encouraged the Spirits to dam the river, kill the animals, and pave the horrible grass with nice smooth asphalt.

MATERIALIST GHOSTS

These Ghosts informed Spirits that there is no life after death and that everything is a hallucination.

BOGIE GHOST

These Ghosts realize they have deteriorated into mere shadows and have now taken up the traditional ghostly role of scaring whomever they can.

Course Notes and Study Format

HOW TO USE THIS GUIDE

The Great Divorce consists of fourteen chapters and can easily be read over the course of a few days.

For best use with the study, each week for eight weeks you will read select chapters from the book, which are approximately five to eight pages each. Each chapter is fairly short and easily digested with the exception of a few. As you read, make notes in your book and underline or highlight sections that interest you. As you work through each session, make note of any other questions you have in the Notes section at the end of each study. The answers to each question can be found at www.BrownChairBooks.com. However, do not cheat yourself. Work through each session prior to viewing the answers.

GROUP FORMAT

For group formats, the study works well over an eight-week period. The first week is an introduction week to hand out study guides (if purchased by the church), read through the introduction and character sketches, and set a plan and schedule for the remaining seven weeks.

SUGGESTED SESSION OUTLINE

Based on the amount of reading each week, we suggest that you follow the study outline below over an eight-week period, but you are by no means locked in to this format. The key is group interest and involvement, not the calendar.

Date	Time	Session	Chapters
		Week 1	Introduction
		Week 2	Preface, Chapters 1 and 2
		Week 3	Chapters 3 and 4
		Week 4	Chapters 5 and 6
		Week 5	Chapters 7 and 8
		Week 6	Chapters 9 and 10
		Week 7	Chapter 11
		Week 8	Chapters 12, 13, and 14

Preface

Have you ever heard the figure of speech, "You can't have your cake and eat it too?" The idea is how difficult it can be to enjoy two things that are usually not possible to have together. For example, "Zach works every night and weekend to pay for his new car that he never has any time to enjoy."

The same can be said about your life when following Christ, as in, "You can't hold on to your sin and live a Christ-like life too." It's either one or the other. The fact is, we must completely reject our sin before the life that God has planned for us can be fully embraced.

> *A life is either all spiritual or not spiritual at all. No man can serve two masters. Your life is shaped by the end you live for. You are made in the image of what you desire.*
>
> **Thomas Merton, Author and Theologian**

1. If we allow our lives to be consumed with bad thoughts and immoral actions, what will eventually happen to our understanding of what is truly right and wrong?

2. Lewis says that there is good and there is evil and that there can be no "legitimate marriage" between the two. What "good" responses might a teenager use to justify the following "bad" behaviors?

a) Cheating is okay as long as ____________________
____

b) Premarital sex is okay as long as ______________
____

c) Drugs and alcohol are okay as long as __________
____

d) Bullying someone is okay as long as ___________
____

3. True or false: God has changed His standards throughout history to accommodate each person, place, and time.

4. Have you ever known someone who believed they could keep doing whatever they wanted while at the same time claiming to be a Christian? How did it work out for them?

5. Read Matthew 5:29–30. On our own personal journey to Heaven, why might it be necessary that we leave our "right hand" and "right eye" behind?

Chapter 1: Next Bus out of Hell

I think if I had a chance to catch the first bus out of Hell, I would be jumping for joy and would be the first person in line! Wouldn't you? We find the exact opposite in this chapter though. In fact, the people in line are argumentative, mean, and generally disagreeable to the point where some even leave the line believing there is a better option.

Perhaps we're really no better. Think about that sin or temptation that God wants you to leave behind, yet for some reason, you just can't seem to let it go. Why is that? Mainly our hesitancy is due to fear. We simply do not trust that God has something better for us.

> *It is not death that a man should fear,*
> *but he should fear never beginning to live.*
> **Marcus Aurelius, Roman Emperor**

1. Describe in detail the mood, atmosphere, images, and depictions of the grey town.

2. The grey town is an imaginative representation of Hell rather than an accurate, biblical representation of the real Hell. If you were to poll your friends, how might they describe Hell?

a) They would say Hell does not exist.
b) It's a place of eternal fire and torture.
c) They would not know.
d) Other______________________________

3. Using the following Bible passages, describe the nature of Hell. In your own words, how would you describe Hell to a friend?

a) Revelation 14:10–11 –

b) 2 Thessalonians 1:9 –

c) Matthew 25:41 –

d) Revelation 20:10 –

4. The messy-haired poet believes he is worthy to take this bus ride to Heaven but the others on the bus are not. How might your friends respond to your criticism of their sin while they see you ignoring you own? What might be a better approach?

5. The souls on the bus complain about the bus driver, saying, “Why can’t he behave naturally?” According to 1 Corinthians 2:14, why do unbelievers have difficulty relating to or understanding a believer’s joy?

Chapter 2: Jabber Jaws

Let's face it. Some of us like to talk more than others. There are others who are quieter and require less conversation. Which are you? Do you like to be in constant communication with others, or do you value your alone time?

This is where Lewis finds himself on his bus ride to Heaven. He wants to visually take in all that he is seeing, yet he cannot escape the conversation of others. It's in this setting that he learns a little more about the grey town, his fellow passengers, and their reasons for wanting to go to Heaven.

> *It was impossible to get a conversation going; everyone was talking too much.*
> **Yogi Berra, Baseball Player**

1. Have you ever known someone who tends to see themselves as the victim of almost every bad situation they find themselves in? Describe the characteristics of someone with a "victim mentality."

2. Describe the messy-haired poet and what led to his death. What do you think he expects to find or receive once he gets to Heaven?

3. What more do we learn about the grey town from the Intelligent Ghost? What connection does the man draw to the length of time people have been in the grey town and their chances of making it to the bus stop?

4. Using a scale of 1 to 10, how would you rate your need for community (the fellowship of others with whom you share common attitudes, interests, and goals) in your life? Why would you choose that rating? Do you think advances in technology (i.e., phones, social media, etc.) have helped or hurt the ability to create a close community?

5. Read Matthew 19:16–22. According to the Intelligent Ghost, the residents of Hell build "unreal" houses that do not keep out the rain or danger. Just like the residents of Hell, what did the rich young ruler believe provided him a "feeling of safety"? What "feelings of safety" might a teenager substitute for Jesus today?

Week 1 Discussion Notes

Answer Guide available at www.BrownChairBooks.com

Chapter 3: Next Stop...Heaven!

We often use the word "Heaven" to express any feeling of euphoria and excitement. For example, one might say, "I can't believe I got free tickets to the concert! I must be in Heaven!"

Scripture does offer us some details, but the fact is, our finite minds cannot fully grasp how magnificent Heaven will actually be!

> *My home is Heaven. I'm just traveling through this world.*
> **Billy Graham, Evangelist**

1. How would you describe Heaven to a friend? How does Lewis describe the landscape of their new destination?

2. Match the following Bible passages with how each describes Heaven.

1) Matthew 6:20	a) No death or sadness
2) Luke 23:43	b) A large place prepared by God for everyone
3) John 14:2	c) Nothing can be destroyed
4) Revelation 21:4	d) Eternal delight

3. As the souls exit the bus, what does Lewis realize about the other passengers as well as himself? How does it affect their interaction with their surroundings?

4. Many of the ghosts were scared to exit the bus or ran back out of fear of the unknown. Has God ever asked you to do something that seemed unreasonable—something that took you into the territory of the unknown? What if God asked you to stop dating someone who you believe is perfect for you? What if God called you to a remote part of the world for mission work instead of accepting a scholarship to the college of your dreams? How would you respond?

5. Describe the appearance of the people who came from Heaven. According to Philippians 3:20–21, how will our bodies be made different in Heaven?

Chapter 4: Who Invited You to Heaven?

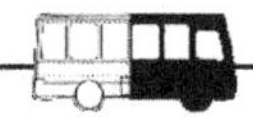

For some reason, people love to judge other people. We judge how they look, what they wear, their actions, and definitely when they mess up.

Judging people is easy, and in some cases, it can even feel good. That is, until we are the object of someone else's judgement. Then we discover how hurtful it can be and why grace and understanding is so important.

> *When you judge others, you do not define them, you define yourself.*
> **Earl Nightingale, Author**

1. Think of someone that you could not imagine running into in Heaven. Explain your reasoning.

2. Describe the earthly relationship between the Big Man and Len the Spirit Guide. What did the Big Man find so hard to believe regarding Len?

3. Which reason below might lead you to doubt the sincerity of someone's Christian confession and why?

a) The confession was made on their death-bed.
b) The person has committed heinous crimes.
c) The person has done something to me personally.
d) The person exhibits no life change.

4. What is the Big Man's definition of a decent person and who should be allowed into Heaven? Why did Len not want the Big Man to continue thinking this way?

5. Read 1 John 1:8–10. The Big Man is self-righteous and believes he is morally superior to Len. He is convinced of his own goodness and sees no reason to repent. If we claim to be good and say that we have not sinned, what do we make God out to be?

Week 2 Discussion Notes

Answer Guide available at www.BrownChairBooks.com

Chapter 5: Debate Time

Do you know someone who loves to debate? No matter what you say, they will generally disagree and try to prove you wrong. This is the exact type of character we find in the Fat, Cultured Ghost in this chapter. Regardless of the facts laid before him and the consequences, he refuses to accept the one truth that would allow him to stay in Heaven for eternity.

I love argument; I love debate. I don't expect anyone just to sit there and agree with me; that's not their job.
Margaret Thatcher, Former British Prime Minister

1. How would you reason with a friend who claims to be a Christian yet argues and debates against key beliefs of the faith, like the virgin birth or the resurrection?

2. What more do we learn about the Fat, Cultured Ghost, and what is his relationship to the Spirit with whom he is talking?

3. According to Dick the Spirit, the Fat, Cultured Ghost's sin is that he was an apostate on Earth. In other words, he was a Christian until he turned his back on the Bible for the modern and popular philosophies of the day because it benefited him. If we go down the road of cherry-picking which Scriptures we think are worth following and which ones are not, what does that do to the Bible as a whole?

4. In Jude verses 3 and 4, Jude tells us how to recognize apostasy and strongly urges those in the body of Christ to fight (or agonize) with everything we have for the faith. What sort of training might you need to be an effective defender of the Christian faith? How comfortable do you feel in your ability to contend for the faith right now?

5. At one point, with unusual intensity, the Spirit tells the Ghost, “We are not playing now.” The Spirit needed to get the Ghost’s attention and warn him that the time has come when all philosophical conversations are over. It is time for absolute truth and a decision based on that truth.

In Romans 13:11, why do you think the Apostle Paul is so adamant that it’s time to wake people up from their spiritual slumber and “stop playing”? When do you think it might be appropriate to use this direct approach with friends or family?

Chapter 6: A Fool’s Gold

During the “Gold Rush” of the 1800s, thousands of people traveled west to mine for gold in hopes of getting rich quickly. As these miners searched in stream beds some found gold and became rich. Others found a shiny mineral called pyrite that glitters and looks like gold but is not. This led to its nickname, fool's gold, because it had no real value.

But even if fool’s gold had real value, if it leads to your making poor choices with the possibility of hurting yourself or others in the process, it’s still foolish.

Wise men don’t need advice. Fools won’t take it.
Benjamin Franklin, Inventor and U.S. Founding Father

1. What does Lewis realize about his current form as he explores Heaven?

2. What was Ikey trying to steal, and what problems did he encounter as a result?

3. What was the Angel's solution to Ikey's desire for an apple? Did he take the Angel up on his suggestion?

4. Greed causes people to do all sorts of things they wouldn't normally do. The love of money is what motivates people to lie, steal, cheat, gamble, embezzle, and even murder. This is illustrated very clearly in the character of Ikey. Imagine that a rich uncle leaves you a million dollars but leaves your siblings nothing. How would you spend the money? What sort of rift do you think it might cause in your relationship with your siblings?

5. The Greek word Jesus used for fool is “aphrōn” and it means “without reason” or “senseless.” Using this definition, why did Jesus refer to the man in Luke 12:16–21 as a fool?

Week 3 Discussion Notes

Answer Guide available at www.BrownChairBooks.com

Chapter 7: A Cynic's Guide to Heaven

A cynical person is suspicious of others because they have been hurt or made to feel vulnerable at some point in their life by someone they trusted. Cynicism can be an easy trap to fall into but difficult to climb out of; if we let it consume us, it can cause us to miss out on some really great opportunities.

Cynicism is also contagious as it brings others down around us and often leads them to avoid us altogether. In this chapter, Lewis discovers first-hand how the cynical attitude of the Hard-Bitten Ghost can discourage his own outlook even while standing in the midst of Heaven.

> *A cynical young person is almost the saddest sight to see, because it means that he or she has gone from knowing nothing to believing nothing.*
> ***Maya Angelou, Poet and Civil Rights Activist***

1. What or who causes you to become cynical and negative? Is it a parent, friend, or event? Explain further.

2. Because the Ghost had become cynical in his earthly life, which conspiracy theory did he develop below?

a) NASA intentionally deceived the public and faked the Apollo moon landing.
b) A flying saucer crashed in Roswell, New Mexico, in 1947, setting up the highly classified military base Area 51.
c) There is a "World Combine" that sets up tourist traps all over the world using advertising and publicity stunts.
d) Elvis Presley faked his death, went into hiding, and is still living to this day.

3. When asked what he would choose, Heaven or Hell, the Hard-Bitten Ghost becomes angry and says that he should not have to change but rather Heaven should adapt to him. According to Ephesians 4:22–24 and Romans 12:2, what type of change is required to truly embrace our life as a Christian?

4. The Hard-Bitten Ghost has become so bitter and unhappy that when paradise in Heaven is finally presented to him, he cannot accept it. C.S. Lewis writes in his book, *Mere Christianity*, “If we find ourselves with a desire that nothing in this world can satisfy, the most probable explanation is that we were made for another world.” Do you think you were made for this world or another? Explain your answer. How will constantly striving for happiness in this world leave one cynical like the Hard-Bitten Ghost?

5. According to Ephesians 4:31–32, how does the Bible teach us to deal with cynicism and bitterness?

Chapter 8: Mirror, Mirror, on the Wall

Face it. We live in a culture obsessed with appearance. We want to be thinner, muscular, and more attractive, and we want to wear the nicest clothes. Then, if you tack on creating the "perfect social media persona," you've just added on a whole new level of complexity.

This obsession to maintain an image can be very stressful. In fact, we can become so self-absorbed with our outward appearance that we become afraid of being transparent about what's going on inside of us for fear of shame and rejection.

> *Vanity can apply to both insecurity and egotism. So I distance myself, because I feel everything.*
> ***Taylor Swift, Singer***

1. In 1 Peter 3:3–4, Peter instructs Christians to focus not so much on our outward appearance, but on the inner, spiritual qualities in order to be truly beautiful. How difficult do you think this is for teenagers, especially teenage girls, in today's culture? Why do you think this is?

2. Describe the Well-Dressed Ghost and what her main issues are with the Bright Spirit that approaches her.

3. God never uses one's outward physical appearance to determine beauty or worth. In 1 Samuel 16:7, what did God instruct the prophet Samuel to examine when searching for the next king of Israel?

4. Why is transparency with God over our sin and shame so important for us if we are to ever experience genuine repentance and God's grace?

5. The Spirit urges the woman to not be afraid to be seen with all of her flaws (inward and outward) and that none of it will matter if she will only learn to exercise her faith and trust God. Read Psalm 139:14. Why is it important that we embrace who we are, flaws and all, in order to exercise our faith?

Week 4 Discussion Notes

Answer Guide available at www.BrownChairBooks.com

Chapter 9: Starstruck

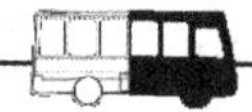

Have you ever met someone famous and suddenly you turn into a bumbling idiot? You start talking too fast, not making sense, or perhaps are unable to speak and just stand there staring uncomfortably at this person.

After witnessing a variety of conversations and actions between Ghosts and Spirits, Lewis is confused, miserable, and somewhat fearful. Then, at last, he is approached by his guiding Spirit who is none other than author, poet, Christian minister, and Lewis's hero, George MacDonald.

> *It would be really great if people would realize that stars are only people with the same weaknesses and flaws, not immaculate idols.*
>
> ***Meg Ryan, Actress***

1. Lewis begins to gush when he unexpectedly encounters his earthly "hero" George MacDonald. What celebrity, musician, athlete, or person throughout history would you become starstruck by if you met them and why?

2. Refrigerium is the idea that damned spirits are given occasional vacations from the torments of Hell with freedom to visit other places. In the book, it appears as though the Ghosts from the grey town take these excursions all the time. What other destinations do they choose?

3. This story seems to suggest that we have a real choice after death—that there is the possibility of salvation for the dead. Read John 5:28–29. What is a Christian's response as to whether or not salvation is determined before we die? What opportunity to visit Heaven did the rich man have after being sent to Hell in Luke 16:19–31?

4. McDonald tells Lewis that "heaven, once attained, works backwards and will turn even that agony into a glory." The fact is, bad things happen regardless of whether we choose Heaven or not. Sometimes the reason is revealed and other times not. Does it bring you comfort to know that everything bad that has ever happened to you will all be better understood once you enter Heaven? Why?

5. According to John 3:19–21, why do people ultimately reject God? How can you know when one of your friends' objections to following Christ is genuine or just a smokescreen to hide the fact that they love their sin?

Chapter 10: Love Hurts

Why is it that the people we know and love the most are also the same people we often hurt the most? Perhaps it's because when we are truly honest about our desires, hopes and dreams with others we expose our weaknesses and set ourselves up to be let down by them.

To protect ourselves, we can decide not to share those details with others to avoid being hurt, but this also guarantees that we will never truly be loved or love another. The risk of opening up and sharing your life with others is that you may get hurt. The reward is that someone may truly know and love you.

I have found the paradox, that if you love until it hurts, there can be no more hurt, only more love.
Mother Teresa, Catholic Nun and Missionary

1. How would you describe the Female Ghost? How would you describe her husband Robert?

2. The Female Ghost carries out her agenda of manipulating her husband all while claiming it's because she loves him. Read 1 Corinthians 13:4–8 and match each characteristic of biblical love with how the wife violated each one below.

1) Love is patient.	a) She was jealous of others and their wealthy.
2) Love is kind.	b) She has a selfish agenda while appearing unselfish.
3) Love does not envy.	c) Her rudeness drives away Robert's friends.
4) Love does not dishonor others.	d) She becomes easily angered with Robert.
5) Love is not self-seeking.	e) She's impatient and drives Robert to make more money.
6) Love is not easily angered.	f) Her hate pleased her when Robert stopped writing.
7) Love keeps no record of wrongs.	g) She is unsympathetic after she ruined Robert's book.
8) Love does not delight in evil.	h) She keeps a laundry list of Robert's wrongs.

3. The Female Ghost needed someone else to validate her life's worth. She never learned to love God or herself and therefore could not love others properly. What forms of abuse might a teenager engage in if they do not like themselves? Why do you think it is important that we learn to love God before we love ourselves?

4. The Female Ghost claims that she "only wants what's best" for Robert. However, no matter how far she pushes him, he never seems to "arrive." Do you think your parents have unreasonable goals for you? Why or why not? How do you know what is reasonable and what might be the selfish agenda of another?

5. How would it change your relationship with others if you practiced 1 Corinthians 13:7 which says, "Love always protects, always trusts, always hopes, always perseveres. Love never fails"?

Week 5 Discussion Notes

Answer Guide available at www.BrownChairBooks.com

Chapter 11a: Motherly Love

(Due to the amount of content and topics covered, Chapter 11 has been divided into two sections, 11a and 11b.)

Have you ever known someone who is your friend only until they get what they want and then suddenly they are nowhere to be found?

Unfortunately, this is often how we treat God. We want what we can get from God—a passing grade, popularity, to make the team, the perfect guy or girl—but then once we get it, our prayer life, Bible reading, and church attendance are gone until another need arises. This is not the relationship that God desires with us, but rather more like that of a close friend whom you talk with each day.

> *We love others best when we love God most.*
> ***Ken Idleman, Pastor and Author***

1. What prevents Pam, the Motherly Ghost, from growing solid? What must she learn to do if she wants to see her son Michael?

2. While she was alive, Pam was so obsessed with her son that she allowed grief to consume her even to the point of keeping his room the same, ignoring the rest of her family, and choosing to live in the past while not letting go. Have you witnessed examples of this in your own life, your family, or friends? How can being unable to let go of our grief impact our relationship with others?

3. Pam angrily claims that she'll love God as long as it brings her back to her son Michael. We should not follow God just to satisfy our own needs, like those who were trying to get food from Jesus in John 6:26–27. What bargains with God might a teenager make if desperate?

4. God commands us to love Him first and others second. Why is it a sin if we get that command turned around, and what could be the result?

5. As MacDonald and Lewis start to move away, MacDonald recites Luke 18:19 when he says, “There is but one good; that is God. Everything else is good when it looks to Him and bad when it turns from Him.” How can normal and natural feelings that God gives us, like love, patriotism, work ethic, intellect, etc., become corrupted and then hurtful to ourselves and others?

Chapter 11b: Leaping Lizards!

Statistics prove that the majority of people who try to give up a substance abuse addiction will fail and relapse within the first couple of days of quitting. It often takes repeated attempts before the individual eventually breaks free for good.

It's not that the addict doesn't see the value in quitting but rather that they hold on to the dangerous idea that there might be some pleasure left in their abuse.

For many of us, our sin is our addiction. We know that giving it up is the right thing to do, but for some reason, we are continually drawn back to it and just cannot seem to let it go on our own. We need the help that only Jesus can offer.

> *Addiction is a hugely complex and destructive disease, and its impact can be simply devastating. All too often, lives and families can be shattered by it.*
> ***Kate Middleton, Duchess of Cambridge***

1. Describe the Dark and Oily Ghost and his pet. What do we later learn that the lizard is a symbol for?

2. What offer does the Angel make to the Ghost, and what must the Ghost do to receive the offer? Read Matthew 7:7, Luke 11:13, and John 14:14. What is the common thread in all these verses about what God wants from us before He acts?

3. Which reason below did the Ghost not give for not wanting his lizard to be killed by the Angel?

1. I don't want to be a bother.
2. Killing it is a bit drastic.
3. It's embarrassing, but look, it's asleep and quiet now.
4. We can consider it later.
5. It's actually not bad but really good for me.
6. Let's just control it gradually over time.
7. I need to see my doctor first.

4. The Angel explains that a gradual approach or delay killing the lizard will not work. It must be done now. Why does the gradual approach to removing sin or temptation from our lives not work?

5. The Angel assures the Ghost that killing the lizard will not kill the Ghost, but what about any pain the Ghost might experience? Read Matthew 18:7–9. How seriously should we approach removing sin?

Week 6 Discussion Notes

Answer Guide available at www.BrownChairBooks.com

Chapter 12: Drama Queen!

Have you ever known someone who seems to blow every situation way out of proportion when given the chance? This type of person generally loves attention and requires excessive amounts of approval and reassurance.

In this chapter, Lewis meets a heavenly woman named Sarah Smith. Frank, her earthly husband, behaves in theatrical, attention-grabbing ways in an attempt to make Sarah feel guilty for her being in Heaven while he is in Hell.

> *I'm terribly attention-seeking. It's very different once you get all this attention, though. Because then you want to control it. And you can't exactly.*
> ***David Williams, Author***

1. How would you describe Sarah Smith? How would you describe her husband, Frank?

2. The Tragedian's alter ego (or persona) was created by Frank as a way to make Sarah feel guilty and to get attention. Why might a teenager create an alter ego or a new identity? Have you ever felt like it would be easier to create a new identity for yourself? If so, why? What are the dangers in doing so, and how hard do you think it is to eventually give it up?

3. There is one new identity that is worth taking on. What do Galatians 2:20 and 2 Corinthians 5:17 teach us about our new nature or "persona" as a believer in Christ? What about our "old self" disappears, and what takes its place? How is Christianity different than other personas we could take on?

4. Sarah tells Frank that she has no needs in Heaven. What do you think it will be like to have no needs? If there are no needs, how will we know what to do? What will we pursue? Will it matter? Read Revelation 7:16–17 for guidance.

5. The Tragedian overreacts to the news that his wife does not need him in Heaven, and he wishes Sarah were dead. In response, Sarah laughs and tells him to rid himself of the foolish Tragedian. How does Frank respond to her laughing? How can laughter often be the best medicine to helping someone see their situation from a different perspective?

Chapter 13: Endless Supply of Joy

It is easy to have faith when you're on top of the world. You're making great grades, you look and feel great, all of your friends and family are doing well—it seems as though nothing can go wrong. Then, without notice, something goes wrong, and your faith is put to the test.

Psalm 30:5 tells us that although weeping may endure for a night, joy will come in the morning. Midnight experiences of testing your faith will come, but each morning brings the opportunity to rely on God's promises and faithfulness to see you through any situation in life.

> *When you rise in the morning, give thanks for the light, for your life, for your strength. Give thanks for your food and for the joy of living. If you see no reason to give thanks, the fault lies in yourself.*
> ***Tecumseh, Indian Chief and Warrior***

1. How would you describe the difference between joy and happiness to a friend?

2. Read James 1:2–4. How is it possible to experience joy in the midst of a painful or difficult situation? What about through sickness or the loss of a loved one?

3. Sarah begs Frank to stop using pity in the wrong way and offers him love and kindness and the opportunity for true joy—but not pity. Read Psalm 72:13 and Luke 10:33. When can pity be an appropriate emotion to show? How is pity different from feeling sorry for someone? When can it become a dangerous weapon?

4. Determined to be joyless, Frank is consumed by the Tragedian, who vanishes in Sarah's bright presence. As Sarah leaves, Lewis asks how Sarah can be untouched by Frank's damnation. What is MacDonald's response? How do you think you would respond watching a loved one choose Hell over Heaven?

5. MacDonald shows Lewis a tiny crack in the soil. All of Hell, MacDonald claims, is contained in this tiny crack. It seems as though, outside of some supernatural expansion, Hell is so small that it cannot be gotten into. With this understanding, how do you picture Heaven in your mind?

Chapter 14: Dream Big!

We all have silly dreams that we simply cannot explain and even wake up laughing about it. There are other times when we are grateful to wake up from a seemingly real nightmare.

Lewis wakens to find that it was all just a dream, and he is now in the "real" world. Ironically though, Lewis's "real" world seems cold and lonely—in fact, not so different from the grey town.

> *I dream of painting and then I paint my dream.*
> ***Vincent Van Gogh, Artist***

1. God used dreams throughout the Bible to speak to His people. Have you ever felt like God was speaking to you through your dreams? Elaborate on this experience and the action you took as a result.

2. Lewis finds himself in the midst of a "great assembly of gigantic forms" all surrounding a silver table with little figures on it like chessmen moving about. Who did the giants, the chessmen, and the table represent? What are the giants doing? What is the purpose of "Time" within the context of the chessboard?

3. MacDonald reveals to Lewis that he has been dreaming this entire time. Why does MacDonald instruct Lewis to make it very clear to other people that his vision of the afterlife was just a dream—not the truth about the afterlife?

4. Read Ephesians 5:13–16. Why is Lewis both surprised and terrified when the sun begins to rise high in the east and he hears voices singing, "Sleepers awake!"? What is his sense of urgency?

5. What do you think is the most important take away from reading the book and completing the study? How would you go about sharing what you have learned with a friend or family member?

Week 7 Discussion Notes

Answer Guide available at www.BrownChairBooks.com

THE SCREWTAPE LETTERS STUDY GUIDE FOR TEENAGERS

A Bible Study for Teens on the
C.S. Lewis Book *The Screwtape Letters*

By Alan Vermilye

The Screwtape Letters Study Guide for Teens takes teenagers through a study of the C.S. Lewis classic, *The Screwtape Letters*.

Created specifically for teenagers, each daily study is designed to take them through each letter written by Screwtape, an undersecretary in the lowerarchy of Hell, to his incompetent nephew Wormwood, a junior devil.

The Screwtape Letters Study Guide for Teens includes:

- Daily Bible study that will take no more than 20 minutes
- Study questions are ideal for group discussion
- Answers to all questions available online
- Ideal for all teenagers
- Easy-to-lead for youth leaders

Learn more at www.BrownChairBooks.com.

THE 90-DAY BIBLE STUDY GUIDE

A Bible Study Tour of the
Greatest Story Ever Told

By Bruce Gust

The Perfect Bible Study Workbook for Beginners!

The 90-Day Bible Study Guide takes you on a journey through select portions of Scripture covering a survey of the Bible in just 90 days! The perfect Bible study for beginners, Bible study for teens, or homeschool groups, adult Bible studies, or those seasoned veterans looking for a refresher Bible study course.

Beginning with Genesis and ending in Revelation, you'll spend just under 30 minutes each day in this Bible Study Guide and workbook on Scripture readings and corresponding Bible study questions designed to guide you to a better understanding of the personalities, the history, the conflicts, the miracles and the truth that is the Christian faith.

Made in the USA
Coppell, TX
22 June 2022